Ready-Set-PN

Editors:

Audrey Knippa, MS, MPH, RN, CNE
Nursing Education Coordinator
Assessment Technologies Institute®, LLC

Sheryl Sommer, PhD, RN
Director Nursing Curriculum and Educational Services
Assessment Technologies Institute®, LLC

Derek Prater, MS Journalism
Lead Product Developer
Assessment Technologies Institute®, LLC

Contributors for Original Edition:

Julia Aucoin, DNS, RN, BC
Assistant Professor
University of North Carolina at Greensboro

Barbara Kuhn Timby, RNC, MA
Nursing Professor
Glen Oaks Community College

Leslie Treas, PhD, RN, CNNP
Assessment Technologies Institute®, LLC

Preparing for the NCLEX-PN® 1

Information About the NCLEX-PN® 1
NCLEX-PN® Registration Process...1
Scheduling the Test – Not Too Soon or Too Late 2
Develop a Study Plan with a Readiness Target......................................3
Review Your Exams 3
Use Your Achievement Tests..3
Read Your Textbooks 3
Complete the NCLEX-PN® Tutorial 3
Stay Healthy..4
Work Schedule 4
Changing Your Appointment 4
Canceling the Test Date 4
Finding the Testing Center 4
What to Bring to the Test 4

The Test 5

Confidentiality 5
Getting Your Results..5

Text Plan for the NCLEX-PN® 6

Client Need Categories..6
Safe and Effective Care Environment 8
Health Promotion and Maintenance 11
Psychosocial Integrity 12
Physiological Integrity 14

Test-Taking Strategies 18

Reading Test Items 18
The Right Answer Is Not There 18
There Are Two Right Answers...18
Cannot Find the Answer You Like 18
Finding the Pattern 18
Priority-Setting Items 19
Client Assignment Items 19
Use Clinical Reasoning..19
What is the Question Asking?..19
Use Maslow's Hierarchy 19
Answer Changers Beware 19
The NCLEX-PN® Hospital 19
Alternate Items 20

Best Wishes from ATI 20

References 20

Preparing for the NCLEX-PN®

Whether you have always wanted to be a nurse or this is second career choice, you have been working hard for some time in a nursing program. However, once you graduate, you still have to pass the NCLEX-PN®. This booklet will introduce you to techniques and tips to help you prepare for the licensure examination.

Join us as we help you get

Ready...Set...Be a Practical Nurse!

To ensure public safety, the granting of licensure to practice as a registered nurse or licensed practical nurse is controlled by regulatory agencies within each U.S. state or territory. The National Council of State Boards of Nursing (NCSBN) develops and administers a licensing examination, which is used by the regulatory agencies to make licensing decisions. To practice as a practical nurse, a candidate must pass the National Council Licensure Examination for Practical Nurses (NCLEX-PN®). This examination measures the candidate's ability be a safe, effective, entry-level practical nurse (PN).

The following groups contribute to the development and administration of the NCLEX® examination: the examination committee, the item review subcommittee, NCSBN NCLEX® examinations staff, and Pearson VUE test services.

Information About the NCLEX-PN®

The NCLEX-PN® Test Plan changes every 3 years.

The current test plan, which provides the major categories and nursing activities of tested content, may be downloaded from the NCSBN Web site at www.ncsbn.org/1287.htm. The most accurate information about completion of the NCLEX-PN® application is in the candidate bulletin, which can be downloaded at www.ncsbn.org/1213.htm A new bulletin is published each January.

NCLEX-PN® Registration Process

1. Candidates must submit an application for licensure to the board of nursing in the state in which they want to be licensed.

   Each state has a process for approving candidates for licensure and determining eligibility for testing. Be sure to follow your school's protocol to prevent a delay in processing. When a candidate has been determined eligible by his state board of nursing this information is forwarded to the NCSBN.

2. All requirements of the state board of nursing must be met.

3. Register with Pearson VUE either through the Internet or by mail.

   a. Internet registration may be completed at www.pearsonvue.com/nclex (select the "Create an Account and register" link).

   b. Registration may be sent through the U.S. Postal Service. The registration form must be mailed along with a certified check, cashier's check, or money order for $200 (made payable to the National Council of State Boards of Nursing) to: NCLEX Operations, PO Box 64950, St. Paul, MN 55164-0950.

Apply to Pearson VUE to take the NCLEX-PN® at the same time as applying to your state board of nursing. You should receive a confirmation of receipt of your application within 1 week. When your approval to test is forwarded to the NCSBN, you will be sent an Authorization to Test (ATT). The ATT will contain your test authorization number, identification number, and expiration date. Your state board of nursing will determine the length of time that the ATT is valid, and this varies from state to state, usually between 60 and 90 days. You will only be able to test within this time period. It cannot be extended for any reason.

Schedule your test date as soon as possible after receiving your ATT. This does not mean you need to test immediately, but test centers fill up rapidly and it may be difficult to get a date that fits your needs. In addition, if you wait too long, there may not be available dates within your valid testing time. As a first-time candidate, you must receive a date within 30 days of your request by phone. If you are repeating the examination, you must be given a test date within 45 days of your request by phone.

Take note: It is important to register with the state board of nursing and apply with Pearson VUE at the same time. This will help assure that when the state board of nursing determines your eligibility and forwards it to Pearson VUE, your application will already be on file.

Scheduling the Test — Not Too Soon or Too Late

A testing time may be scheduled after you receive the ATT. Scheduling can be accomplished through www.pearsonvue.com/nclex or by calling NCLEX® candidate services at one of the telephone numbers listed on the inside cover of the candidate bulletin.

Be realistic when scheduling the test. Avoid times that might be extremely stressful. A month to transition from school should be adequate to prepare for the test. During this time, review course materials and class notes, practice many questions, and then test. Waiting more than 5 months can cause confidence to diminish and distract you from your purpose. Schedule the exam within a reasonable time frame to increase your chances of success.

While you should choose several possible dates for testing, be sure to identify and select only your best time of day. Go to www.pearsonvue.com/nclex to find testing center locations. Look into the location of several testing centers and their ease of access from your home, so that you have more than one option of sites. Please note that you can test in any city or state — the testing center is not linked to your state of initial licensure. Before making the call, have a list of sites and dates and your preferred time of day.

Develop a Study Plan with a Readiness Target

It is ideal to set a target of 1 week before the test to have reached your study goals. Use results from the ATI comprehensive assessments and predictors to identify content areas to focus your study. Be sure to complete the focused review soon after completing the comprehensive predictor. Use class notes, the ATI Content Mastery Series™ review modules, online testing, and the ATI-PLAN™ DVD series. Focus on content that needs review. Breaking down your study plan into manageable goals will make it easier to achieve your target date. If you enroll in Virtual ATI®, your instructor will assist you to make a plan and set a date.

Review Your Exams

When faculty offer you a test review session before or after exams, take advantage of this opportunity. Review sessions before exams will help you focus your study efforts. Review sessions after exams will help you obtain more information about missed items, so that the content can be clearly understood.

Use Your Achievement Tests

Standardized achievement tests have been selected by the faculty to help you prepare for the NCLEX-PN®. They serve as a validation of your application of knowledge as well as a guide for areas to be studied. Putting forth your best efforts on achievement tests can provide you with confidence as you approach the NCLEX-PN®. Scores for tests can be interpreted with assistance from the faculty. Results can be used to improve your test-taking skills and to focus your study efforts on specific content areas. Take your achievement tests seriously and participate in reviewing the results.

Read Your Textbooks

How can the resources provided by your faculty be used most effectively? Read assignments prior to class. After class, go back to textbooks and reread the tables, trace through the figures and diagrams, discuss the care plans and maps, and respond to the critical-thinking questions and case studies. This will help you focus on relevant information that will support your NCLEX-PN® preparation. When studying for remediation, review the related content mastery book and go back to textbooks to read the content again.

Complete the NCLEX-PN® Tutorial

Go to www.pearsonvue.com/nclex and scroll down to the PLAY TUTORIAL button. Even though you will be going through this tutorial on your test day, the more familiar you become with the NCLEX-PN® screens and processes, the easier the test can seem. Practice using the calculator on the computer.

Stay Healthy

Do activities that keep you healthy and feeling well. This may include exercise, eating well, reading, practicing relaxation techniques, and visiting with family and friends. Drink plenty of water the day before the test and before the test, and bring water to drink at the programmed breaks. You may also bring a light snack to eat. If you typically consume caffeine, you may ingest a light or moderate amount prior to the test, as this substance can affect your performance. Be sure to get adequate rest the night before the test.

Work Schedule

Discuss your test date with your employer. If possible, request time off the week before the test to allow for adequate rest.

Changing Your Appointment

If you choose to change your appointment, you must do this at least one full business day before your test is scheduled. For example, a test scheduled for 10:00 a.m. Monday must be changed by 10:00 a.m. the Friday before. There is no charge for this change. Any changes after that point will result in forfeiting the examination fee. You must reschedule online at www.pearsonvue.com/nclex or by phone. If you have special accommodations, you must contact the NCLEX-PN® program coordinator, just as you did to originally schedule. If you do not arrive on time, you also forfeit your time slot and examination fee, and you must register and pay again.

Canceling the Test Date

Canceling the test date is a very difficult decision and should be made only after considering all of the options. Regardless of the reason, you will forfeit the test fees and need to reapply and pay the fees again.

Finding the Testing Center

To find the address of your testing location, go to www.pearsonvue.com/ppt. You can get directions on the Internet by using a map search engine. Be sure you know where you are going ahead of time and allow enough time for travel whether driving or taking public transportation.

What to Bring to the Test

You must bring your Authorization to Test and a valid picture identification with your signature to the testing center. Without this information, you won't be permitted to test. You will forfeit your testing appointment and fee and will need to reschedule and pay a testing fee again. Your fingerprint and photo will be taken at the testing center, and you will be asked to provide your signature.

No study materials may be brought into the testing facility. You will be issued a locker for your backpack or purse. Snacks, identification, and personal-needs items can be stored in the locker. Turn off your cell phone and/or pager. No calculators will be allowed; there will be one on the computer for your use.

The Test

The NCLEX-PN® examination uses Computerized Adaptive Testing (CAT) to distribute the test items. Each time you answer a question, the computer determines the next question based on the difficulty of the prior question and whether your response was correct or incorrect. For example, if you get an item correct, the next question becomes more difficult. If you get it wrong, the next question becomes easier. The idea is for you to demonstrate a pattern of competency in answering the more difficult items. Since items are targeted to ability, fewer items are needed to produce test results that are stable. It is expected that you will only answer about 50% of the questions correctly, so you will want to establish that pattern of competency early and maintain it.

The examinee must answer a minimum of 85 questions but may be required to answer up to 205 questions. The test will be finished when the computer determines with 95% certainty that your ability is either below or above the passing standard, the maximum amount of time has elapsed, or the maximum number of questions has been answered.

The total time allowed for the test is 5 hours. There will be two optional breaks, one after 2 hours of testing and another after 3½ hours of testing. If you feel you need a break, it may be to your advantage to take one. Time away from the test may help you feel more refreshed and ready to continue. It is important to remember that time spent on breaks is deducted from the total testing time.

The questions appear on the computer screen one at a time. There is no time limit per question, but it is important to keep a steady pace when testing. If you do not know the answer, make your best guess and move on. The test will not progress if you do not pick an answer for each question. You can change your answer as many times as you like until you select the confirm key. Once you have done that, the next question will appear. You cannot go back to any previous questions.

Confidentiality

You will be asked to agree to maintain the confidentiality of all test items. This means that posting, sharing, or discussing items that you remember could result in legal action.

Getting Your Results

Visit your state board of nursing Web site to find out the best method for getting your results. All states will provide written notification of your results with appropriate documentation by ground mail. In the event you were not successful, you may retest after meeting the waiting period required by your state.

Test Plan for the NCLEX-PN®

The NCLEX-PN® is constructed according to a test plan that provides a framework for the scope and content of the examination questions. The breadth of content is based on data from the most recent practice analysis (*2006 LPN/VN Practice Analysis*). The NCLEX-PN® includes application-based scenarios in the clinical areas of medical-surgical, maternal newborn, nursing care of children, and mental health nursing. Several additional concepts and processes fundamental to safe and effective practice at the entry level are integrated into the NCLEX-PN®, including:

- Nursing Process – a scientific problem-solving approach to client care that includes data collection, planning, implementation, and evaluation.
- Caring – interaction of the nurse and client in an atmosphere of mutual respect and trust. In this collaborative environment, the nurse provides hope, support, and compassion to help achieve desired outcomes.
- Communication and Documentation – verbal and nonverbal interactions between the nurse and the client, the client's family, and the other members of the health care team. Events and activities associated with client care are validated in written or electronic records that reflect quality and accountability in the provision of care.
- Teaching/Learning – facilitation of the acquisition of knowledge, skills, and attitudes promoting a change in behavior.

Client Need Categories

The test plan is organized into categories referred to as "client needs." This is a comprehensive classification system that defines nursing actions and competencies across all settings for all clients.

The items on the NCLEX-PN® are distributed according to established percentages among four major categories of client needs:

Safe and Effective Care Environment

    Coordinated Care 12-18%

    Safety and Infection Control 8-14%

Health Promotion and Maintenance 7-13%

Psychosocial Integrity 8-14%

Physiological Integrity

    Basic Care and Comfort 11-17%

    Pharmacological Therapies 9-15%

    Reduction of Risk Potential 10-16%

    Physiological Adaptation 11-17%

The majority of items are written at the application level of cognitive ability (which requires more complex thought processing) or higher. The average reading level for the exam is 10th grade. The NCLEX-PN® is not intended to test the ability of the candidate to read, but to determine the level of proficiency in understanding nursing concepts and activities.

The table on the following page demonstrates the NCLEX-PN® test plan as it utilizes the four major categories of client needs. The percentage of items is based on the results of the practice analysis study and judgment from a panel of experts. Items in the NCLEX-PN® test plan are not limited exclusively to the examples on the following pages. More specific information and publications on test content are available from the National Council of State Boards of Nursing, Inc., 111 E. Wacker Drive, Suite 2900, Chicago, IL 60601 or at www.ncsbn.org.

Client Needs

Safe and Effective Care Environment

Coordinated Care 12–18%	Examples of Related Content
	<ul><li>Advance Directives</li><li>Advocacy</li><li>Client Care Assignments</li><li>Client Rights</li><li>Collaboration with Interdisciplinary Team</li><li>Concepts of Management and Supervision</li><li>Confidentiality/Information Security</li><li>Continuity of Care</li><li>Establishing Priorities</li><li>Ethical Practice</li><li>Informed Consent</li><li>Information Technology</li><li>Legal Responsibilities</li><li>Performance Improvement (Quality Improvement)</li><li>Referral Process</li><li>Resource Management</li><li>Staff Education</li></ul>

Safe and Effective Care Environment <small>continued</small>

Test Item Topics
<ul><li>Advocating for clients</li><li>Accessing client records using facility regulations</li><li>Assigning client care delivery</li><li>Assisting new employee during orientation</li><li>Collaborating with interdisciplinary team when providing care</li><li>Collecting data and prioritizing care for assigned group of clients</li><li>Documenting client data using computerized format</li><li>Demonstrating telephone triage</li><li>Ensuring confidentiality and privacy of clients</li><li>Identifying and reporting client conditions (e.g., physical or sexual abuse, communicable disease) per agency policy</li><li>Making clinical decisions using data from various sources</li><li>Participating in informed consent process</li><li>Participating in performance evaluations of other staff by providing input</li><li>Participating in quality assurance activities</li><li>Participating in the development and revision of client's plan of care</li><li>Participating in transcription of primary care provider orders, including verbal and phone orders</li><li>Promoting client involvement in care decision making</li><li>Providing care using research</li><li>Providing follow-up to client/family after discharge</li><li>Reinforcing teaching to the client/family regarding advance directives</li><li>Reporting a health care provider's unsafe practice activities (e.g., improper care, substance abuse, inappropriate words/actions to clients or families)</li><li>Seeking assistance when unable to perform assigned tasks</li><li>Transferring and discharging clients according to agency policies</li><li>Using information technology in various health care settings</li><li>Using proper chain of command when assisting with resolution of staff conflict</li></ul>

Client Needs

Safe and Effective Care Environment

Safety and Infection Control 8–14%	Examples of Related Content
	• Accident/Error/Injury prevention • Ergonomic Principles • Handling Hazardous and Infectious Materials • Home Safety • Internal and External Disaster Plans • Medical and Surgical Asepsis • Reporting of Incident/Event/Irregular Occurrence/Variance • Restraints and Safety Devices • Safe Use of Equipment • Security Plan • Standard/Transmission-Based/Other Precautions

Test Item Topics

- Adhering to standard procedures for handling biohazardous materials
- Applying restraints safely with use of least-restrictive devices, until no longer needed
- Checking the accuracy and appropriateness of treatment orders
- Collecting data regarding client allergies and documenting in the medical record
- Confirming identity of the client
- Following agency policy when handling hazardous conditions in work environment (e.g., chemical or blood spill)
- Maintaining medical/surgical asepsis as needed
- Implementing appropriate monitoring procedures (e.g., restraint checks, seizure precautions)
- Operating and maintaining equipment safely, such as the operation of a suctioning device
- Participating in preparation and implementation of internal/external disaster plans
- Preparing a variance report or irregular occurrence/incident report
- Providing care using ergonomic principles
- Providing information to client/family on ways to maintain safety in the home
- Providing for safety by searching client belongings when indicated
- Reinforcing teaching to the client/family on how to use health care equipment and other safety precautions
- Reinforcing teaching to the client on ways to prevent stress injuries
- Using standard precautions when providing care

Client Needs

Health Promotion and Maintenance

Percentage of Test 7–13 %	Examples of Related Content
	<ul><li>Aging Process</li><li>Ante/Intra/Postpartum and Newborn Care</li><li>Data Collection Techniques</li><li>Developmental Stages and Transitions</li><li>Disease Prevention</li><li>Expected Body Image Changes</li><li>Family Planning</li><li>Health Promotion/Screening Programs</li><li>High Risk Behaviors</li><li>Human Sexuality</li><li>Immunization</li><li>Lifestyle Choices</li><li>Self-Care</li></ul>

Test Item Topics

- Assisting the client/family to make choices regarding beginning of life/end of life
- Assisting the client/family to make choices regarding family planning
- Caring for the prenatal client, including prenatal fetal monitoring
- Choosing developmentally appropriate nursing interventions for clients of various ages (e.g., birth to 1 yr, 1 to 3 yr, 3 to 5 yr, 5 to 12 yr, 12 to 20 yr, 20 to 40 yr, 40 to 60 yr, greater than 60 yr)
- Determining the client's ability to perform self-care activities
- Identifying barriers to learning and communicating
- Monitoring the client in labor
- Participating in data collection for admission, baseline, and ongoing assessments
- Participating in planning and implementing health promotion programs (e.g., smoking cessation, weight management, stress management, immunization for children and adults)
- Promoting participation in health screening programs
- Providing care to the client following delivery
- Providing the client with information regarding high risk behaviors
- Providing newborn care including cord care, circumcision, and infant nutrition
- Reinforcing teaching to the client/family about immunization schedules
- Reinforcing teaching to the client on the importance of self-examination screening techniques

Client Needs

Psychosocial Integrity

Percentage of Test	Examples of Related Content
8–14%	<ul><li>Abuse or Neglect</li><li>Behavioral Management</li><li>Coping Mechanisms</li><li>Crisis Intervention</li><li>Cultural Awareness</li><li>End of Life Concepts</li><li>Grief and Loss</li><li>Mental Health/Illness Concepts</li><li>Religious or Spiritual Influences on Health</li><li>Sensory/Perceptual Alterations</li><li>Situational Role Changes</li><li>Stress Management</li><li>Substance-Related Disorders</li><li>Suicide/Violence Precautions</li><li>Support Systems</li><li>Therapeutic Communication</li><li>Therapeutic Environment</li><li>Unexpected Body Image Changes</li></ul>

Psychosocial Integrity continued

Test Item Topics
• Assisting the client in adjusting to changes in body image to promote recovery
• Collecting data from the client with suspected substance abuse/chemical dependency, withdrawal, or toxicity
• Communicating with the client who is not following treatment plan
• Determining the client's potential for committing acts of violence
• Developing therapeutic relationships with the client and family and promoting positive self-esteem
• Encouraging client participation in group sessions
• Examining reasons for the client's behavior
• Offering emotional support to client/family
• Offering guidance during times of crisis
• Participating in the care of the client with non-substance related dependencies
• Participating in planning and intervening for the client/family during end-of-life care
• Participating in various types of therapies (e.g., reminiscence and validation therapies)
• Promoting effective coping of client/family
• Providing care for the client/family based on cultural beliefs regarding health practices
• Providing care for the client/family who is at risk for or has been abused
• Providing support during times of grief and loss
• Providing therapeutic environment to manage behavior
• Recognizing needs of the client with distorted sensory perceptions
• Reinforcing teaching to assist the caregivers/family of clients with mental illness in controlling undesirable, disruptive, or destructive behaviors
• Reinforcing teaching to the client/family regarding client condition

Client Needs

Physiological Integrity

Basic Care and Comfort 11–17%	Examples of Related Content
	<ul><li>Assistive Devices</li><li>Elimination</li><li>Mobility/Immobility</li><li>Nonpharmacological Comfort Interventions</li><li>Nutrition and Oral Hydration</li><li>Palliative/Comfort Care</li><li>Personal Hygiene</li><li>Rest and Sleep</li></ul>

Test Item Topics

- Administering tube feedings safely
- Assisting the client with selecting foods appropriate for diet and health status
- Assisting with moving clients using appropriate proper body mechanics and assistive devices
- Assisting with ambulation, elimination, feeding, hygiene, and dressing as needed
- Collecting and recording intake and output data
- Implementing measures to promote healthy skin integrity
- Integrating alternative/complementary methods to manage health
- Intervening for the client with sleep/rest needs
- Promoting methods for normal urinary and bowel elimination
- Providing for client/family palliative care needs
- Providing for the client's nutritional and hydration needs
- Providing care to maximize the client's mobility
- Providing care to the client in traction or other immobilizing devices
- Providing measures for pain relief and comfort using nonpharmacologic measures

Client Needs

Physiological Integrity

Pharmacological Therapies 9–15%	Examples of Related Content
	• Adverse Effects • Contraindications and Compatibilities • Dosage Calculations • Expected Effects • Medication Administration • Pharmacological Actions • Pharmacological Agents • Side-Effects

Test Item Topics

- Monitoring the client receiving a blood transfusion
- Following agency protocol for maintaining accurate documentation of medication administration using a medication administration record (MAR)
- Following protocol to phone in client prescription to pharmacy
- Following regulations when administering and disposing of controlled substances
- Identifying precautions for medications the client receives
- Monitoring the rate and for possible complications of intermittent or continuous infusions
- Preparing and administering medications via oral, nasogastric, topical, subcutaneous, intramuscular, intravenous, conjunctival, buccal, nasal, or rectal routes
- Properly calculating medication doses and infusion rates
- Recognizing data to collect prior to medication administration
- Recognizing precautions and contraindications for clients when administering medications
- Reviewing pharmacological agents regarding the client's pathophysiology
- Using the six rights when administering medications

Client Needs

Physiological Integrity

Reduction of Risk Potential	Examples of Related Content
10–16%	<ul><li>Diagnostic Tests</li><li>Laboratory Values</li><li>Potential for Alterations in Body Systems</li><li>Potential for Complications of Diagnostic Tests/Treatments/Procedures/Surgery or Health Alterations</li><li>Therapeutic Procedures</li><li>Vital Signs</li></ul>

Test Item Topics

- Caring for clients undergoing procedures and/or treatments and providing assistance as necessary
- Collecting client data as indicated by situation (e.g., vital signs, oxygen saturation, neurological and circulatory checks)
- Collecting data of client risk potential based on potential for falls, mobility status, and sensory impairments
- Inserting and caring for various types of tubes (e.g., nasogastric, indwelling urinary catheter)
- Monitoring the client following an unusual occurrence (e.g., fall, medication error)
- Monitoring the client for alterations in body systems
- Performing an electrocardiogram (ECG) and intervening as directed
- Performing specimen collection for diagnostic testing (e.g., stool, urine, sputum)
- Providing care and maintaining safety for the client undergoing surgery
- Providing care to the client with continuous or intermittent nasogastric suction
- Providing preoperative and postoperative care

16

Client Needs

Physiological Integrity

Physiological Adaptation 11–17%	Examples of Related Content
	• Alterations in Body Systems • Basic Pathophysiology • Fluid and Electrolyte Imbalances • Medical Emergencies • Radiation Therapy • Unexpected Response to Therapies

Test Item Topics

- Detecting abnormalities on the client's cardiac monitor strip
- Intervening when intravenous line infiltration is detected
- Monitoring and documenting the client's fluid and electrolyte status
- Monitoring the client for signs and symptoms of an infection
- Notifying primary care provider when change in client status
- Performing cardiopulmonary resuscitation
- Providing care for the newborn requiring phototherapy
- Providing care to the client requiring a tracheostomy
- Providing care to the client requiring intervention to improve respiratory status (e.g., breathing treatment, suctioning, repositioning)
- Providing care for the client with an unexpected response to therapy
- Providing emergency care for clients with injury/trauma
- Providing respiratory care to the client receiving mechanical ventilation
- Providing wound care (e.g., surgical, burns) including removal of wound sutures or staples
- Reinforcing teaching to the client experiencing side/adverse effects of radiation therapy
- Responding expediently and appropriately to the client experiencing choking or respiratory distress

Test-Taking Strategies

Reading Test Items

The amount of information in the item can be overwhelming and the responses can confuse you. It is best to read the stem of the question, develop a pool of answers from your total body of knowledge, then search through the responses for the one response that was in your pool of answers.

The Right Answer Is Not There

When reading the responses to an item, your first choice may not be there. Since the NCLEX-PN® expects you to know the best answer; the responses may list the second or third choice as the expected answer. This is why you need a pool of answers from which to draw. Haphazard guessing can be disastrous, as there is only a 25% chance that you will guess correctly.

There Are Two Right Answers

You've got it narrowed down to two responses you think are correct. Before selecting the best response, reread the stem of the item and be sure you know what the item is asking. For standard four-option multiple choice questions, the writers and reviewers intend for only one answer to be correct. Answers are either right or wrong. None of these items is keyed for two responses.

Cannot Find the Answer You Like

If, after narrowing down your choices to two and rereading the stem, you still cannot find an answer you like, you must select one and move on. Every item must be answered in order to move ahead in the test. While there is no penalty for guessing, there is reward in narrowing down the responses and giving it your best shot. Try not to stay on an item you're unsure of for more than your allotted minute. It could disrupt your thinking and make it hard to get back on track.

Finding the Pattern

There are many myths circulating about the NCLEX-PN®, such as that certain preselected candidates will get 205 items or that, when in doubt, candidates should choose answer C. There are no patterns for correct answers – a relatively equal number of As, Bs, Cs, and Ds are used as item responses. There has also been speculation that if, for example, you miss a renal question, you will get a dozen more like it. In reality, you tend to remember the items you don't know, so it only seems that these kinds of items continue to appear. There is no pattern of topics – the test items must follow the distribution of the test plan.

Priority-Setting Items

To answer a priority item (i.e., "Which one will you do first?"), you must recognize that it is likely that all four responses are correct and represent actions you should take. However, you can only choose one of these options, so you must choose the one and only one action that you should do first to protect the client.

Client Assignment Items

When answering a client assignment item, you will find that all four clients need your attention. However, you can only choose one of these options. So you must choose the client who is the least stable or will be in trouble first (or is likely to die first) if you don't attend to the care. Using this cue, you can generally identify the priority client.

Use Clinical Reasoning

If you have never heard of the medication in the item, it may not matter. For example, the item tells you the medication is causing nausea and vomiting. What do you do for any client who is nauseous after taking a medication? Giving medication with food often helps. When in doubt, use your clinical reasoning skills to lead you to the correct response.

What is the Question Asking?

Be sure you recognize who is the subject of the question: the client, the family, or the nurse. Also recognize that you are the practical nurse in most questions. If the question refers to a coworker, you are the one who is delegating to licensed practical (vocational) nurses or assistive personnel.

Use Maslow's Hierarchy

Be familiar with Maslow's hierarchy of needs and use it when asked to prioritize care. Physiological needs (e.g., air, water, food) always come before other needs (e.g., safety and security).

Answer Changers Beware

In your test-taking experience, you may have changed the correct answer to a wrong answer because you second-guessed yourself. As a strong nurse, you should exercise sound reasoning, but do not underestimate your abilities.

The NCLEX-PN® Hospital

If a supply or piece of equipment is included in the item, then consider it available for your use. If a medication is included, expect that it is in the formulary and there is an order. Also, there is no such thing as being short staffed in the NCLEX-PN® hospital; nurses always have time to sit at eye level with clients and listen to them.

Alternate Items

While only about 2 to 3% of the average 110 items on the NCLEX-PN® examination are alternate items, it is helpful to be familiar with this style of non-multiple-choice format before taking the test. The tutorial will help you with this. There are five types of alternate-item formats. These are:

- Fill-in-the-blank items, often a calculation requiring you to list an amount as a response. The unit of measure will already be in the item for you.
- Drag and drop items, which ask you to put steps in order of importance for a procedure or intervention.
- Chart review items, which provide information in three tabs that you must read to respond to the item.
- Hot-spot items, which require you to use your computer mouse to select an area within a picture that accurately reflects the correct response. Only one area will be the correct response.
- Multiple response items, which require you to select from two to all possible answers. You must choose all the responses that apply; no partial credit is given for getting the item half right.

Best Wishes from ATI

If you have pursued a diligent plan for your NCLEX-PN® study throughout your nursing program, you will go into the licensure exam equipped for success. The ATI Content Mastery Series™ review modules, online testing, ATI-PLAN™ DVD series, and results from diagnostic assessments are designed to support you in your preparation and provide you with the review materials you need to pass. Use the materials on a consistent basis. Go into the NCLEX-PN® with strength and confidence. Success is within your grasp.

Ready... Set... Be a Practical Nurse!

References

National Council of State Boards of Nursing. (2008). *2008 NCLEX® Examination Candidate Bulletin.* Retrieved March 25, 2008, from https://www.ncsbn.org/1213.htm

National Council of State Boards of Nursing. (2007). *Report of findings from the 2006 LPN/VN practice analysis linking the NCLEX-PN® to practice* (Research Brief Vol. 28). Chicago: Author.